Mal
Love

Born in Yorkshire in 1953, Annie Lawson studied Fine Art Printmaking at Sheffield Art College before moving to London to sell knitted bumblebees from a stall at Camden Lock. She moved from the bees to poetry on postcards and then on to cartoons. Since 1988 her cartoon collections have been published by Deirdre McDonald Books, and her cartoon strip *The Big Girls* ran for a year in the weekend *Guardian*. Her work has also appeared in the *Observer*, *City Limits* and *Honey* magazine.

It is now possible to buy Annie Lawson books, T-shirts and postcards at her main trading outlet, a stall at Covent Garden Apple Market, as well as at other selected outlets.

Male-order Love

by

Annie Lawson

PENGUIN BOOKS

PENGUIN BOOKS

Published by the Penguin Group
Penguin Books Ltd, 27 Wrights Lane, London w8 5tz, England
Penguin Putnam Inc., 375 Hudson Street, New York, New York 10014, USA
Penguin Books Australia Ltd, Ringwood, Victoria, Australia
Penguin Books Canada Ltd, 10 Alcorn Avenue, Toronto, Ontario, Canada m4v 3b2
Penguin Books (NZ) Ltd, Private Bag 102902, NSMC, Auckland, New Zealand

Penguin Books Ltd, Registered Offices: Harmondsworth, Middlesex, England

First published in Penguin Books 1998
1 3 5 7 9 10 8 6 4 2

Some of these cartoons first appeared in *Brilliant Advice*,
More Brilliant Advice, *Biological Function* and *I Talk to Cats* all by
Annie Lawson and published by Deirdre McDonald Books

Printed in England by Clays Ltd, St Ives plc

Dear Special Best Friend...

BEST
HONESTLY, MEN! /FOOTBALL/FOOTBALL /FOOTBALL/BEER/BEER/BEER /BURPING AND FARTING IN FRONT OF US/THEY'RE SO DISGUSTING!
CHOCOLATE
CHOCOLATE
CRISPS
CRISPS
CRISPS
BURP
BANANA CAKE
WINE
FART
FRIENDS

OK, WE'VE DONE TWO MINUTES ON THE SENSIBLE, GROWN-UP TOPICS...

NOW LET'S GET STUCK INTO THE GOSSIP!

Seeing
YOUR MOTHER

AN ILLUSTRATION OF **HOW DIFFICULT IT IS** TO GIVE ADVICE TO A FRIEND, WHO, AS A CONSEQUENCE OF SPLITTING UP WITH SOMEONE, IS NOW **UTTERLY DESPERATE** TO MEET SOMEONE ELSE...

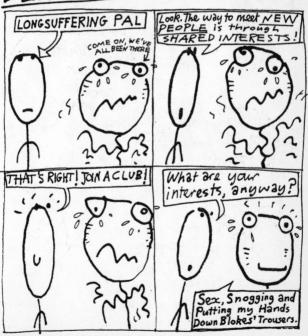

Talk To Your Children!

AN ILLUSTRATION OF <u>HOW DANGEROUS</u> <u>+ EASY</u> IT IS TO MENTALLY ADOPT SELF-DEFEATING BELIEF-PATTERNS AND THUS <u>ACTIVATE CYCLES OF NEGATIVITY</u> IN YOUR LIFE:—

STRESSED WITH YOUR FLATMATE?

DO THIS EXERCISE :-

PLONK DOWN AND DON'T SPEAK ALL NIGHT.

JANICE, YOU'VE GOT TO ASK YOURSELF ONE QUESTION ABOUT THIS RELATIONSHIP WITH JEREMY: "WHAT ARE YOU GETTING OUT OF IT?"
Why do I always wince when she says that?

Teach Your Cat To Read

ELIZABETH BARRETT BROWNING

How do I love thee?
Let me count the ways.

I love thee to the
depth and breadth
and height

My soul can reach,
when feeling out of sight

For the ends of Being
and ideal Grace.

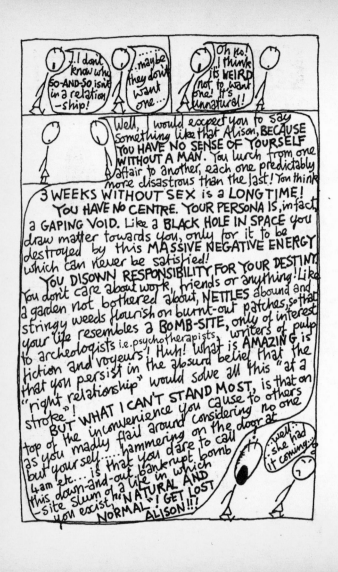

WE PLOD THROUGH LIFE ALL DRY & PARCHED...

COUGH!

... WHEN THERE'S "GOSSIP FAMINE"...
THEN, LO & BEHOLD, SOMEONE GOES AND MAKES
A COMPLETE PRAT OF THEMSELVES!

HOORAY!

HA HA!   2! ! / Ho! HO!   HEE HEE!

OOPS!

I Socialise,
therefore
I AM!

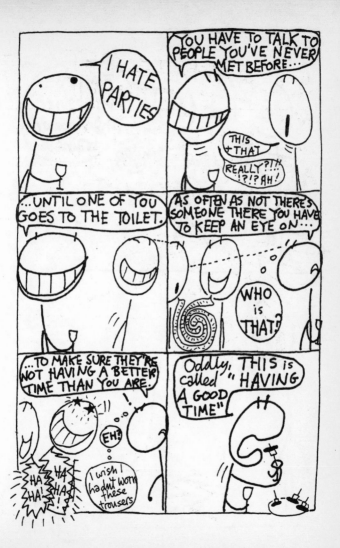

WHAT DO WOMEN TALK ABOUT?

ALAN THINKS THAT Women On Their Own TALK ABOUT THEIR BOTTOMS...

Here, **ALAN** sits absolutely still and quiet, in the hope that **THE WOMEN** will forget he's there and commence **THE BOTTOM- TALK**.

FLIRTING

The person who rattles on interminably about HERSELF in an attempt to appear ALL-INDEPENDENT-SEEMING will not get off with The Desired Object. REMEMBER :- THE DESIRED OBJECT IS MORE INTERESTED IN HIMSELF THAN YOU.*

..I'm doing this + that.... WOOOOO... ...EXCITING!

*Applies to lesbians also

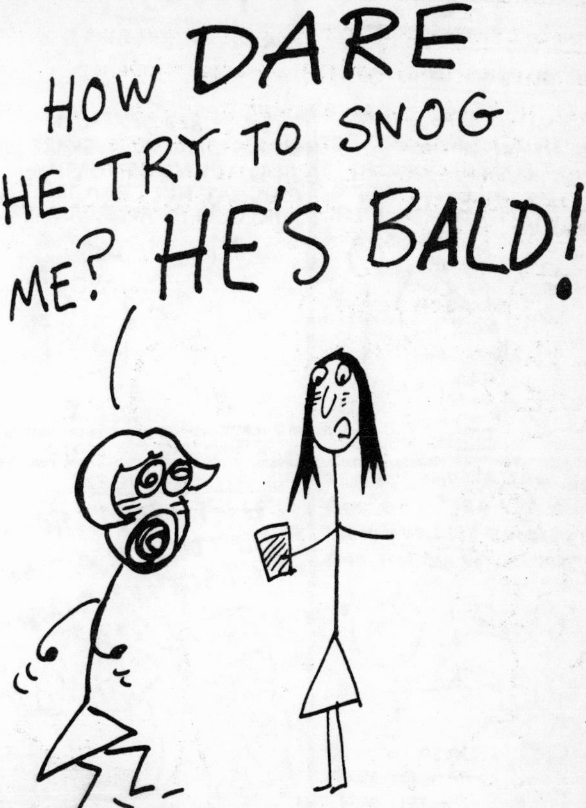
HOW DARE HE TRY TO SNOG ME? HE'S BALD!

FLIRTING

Troubleshooting (ii)

The person who gushes extra-effusively over The Desired Object's *physical* beauty WILL NOT GET OFF WITH THE DESIRED OBJECT.

... oh you have A GORGEOUS NOSE and GORGEOUS HAIR and what A GORGEOUS BODY... etc.

THE DESIRED OBJECT IS NOT BLIND: HE IS AWARE THAT THE VISOG STARING BACK AT HIM FROM THE MIRROR IS NOT ROBERT REDFORD'S. *

* EXCEPTION: MEN AND LESBIANS WHO THINK THEY'RE IT. AVOID.

HE WILL ASSUME, HOWEVER, THAT YOU ARE "BLIND" AND THEREFORE IN LOVE, WHICH OF COURSE YOU ARE NOT, ONLY "IN LIKE."

you are her hero.

HIS EGO, TICKLED INTO A WAKEFUL STATE BY YOUR FLATTERY, WILL TELL HIM, "SHE THINKS YOU ARE A GOLDEN GOD."

THE CONSEQUENCE:
TERROR-STATIONS!!!
POTENTIAL "FATAL ATTRACTION" SCENARIO!!!

**** me, or I'LL BOIL YOUR RABBIT!

HANDCUFFED + CHAINED.

FLIRTING
(including lesbians)

Troubleshooting (iii)

The person who acts all cool and virtually IGNORES The Desired Object, in order to whet his curiosity, WILL NOT GET OFF WITH THE DESIRED OBJECT:

This is because they were "Demand-Fed" as babies, and were picked up when squawking.

oh, poor baby!

AAAAAA AAAIEEE!

BABY

MOTHER

GRANDMOTHER

LEAVE HIM! DON'T PICK HIM UP! BEST HE LEARNS SOONER THAN LATER!

No mother, that's cruel!

The adage "Treat them like shit and they'll stick like shit to your feet" is bad advice in "ME-GENERATION" flirtation situations.

oh, let me give you Tender Loving Care!

"ME-GENERATION-ISTS" expect lots of TLC from their lovers, and will immediately seek out pastures new if god forbid the TLC ever dries up.

IGNORING the person you fancy will only make him think you're a cold icicle. (This may work if he was born before 1960.)

TURN ME ON! FREEZE ME OUT!

HOW DO YOU KNOW IT'S COOL FOR BALD MEN TO SHAVE THEIR HEADS?
MAYBE IT'S ACTUALLY COOLER FOR THEM TO HAVE PONYTAILS!
CRITICAL FACULTIES APPROACHING MELTDOWN
HOW DO YOU KNOW?

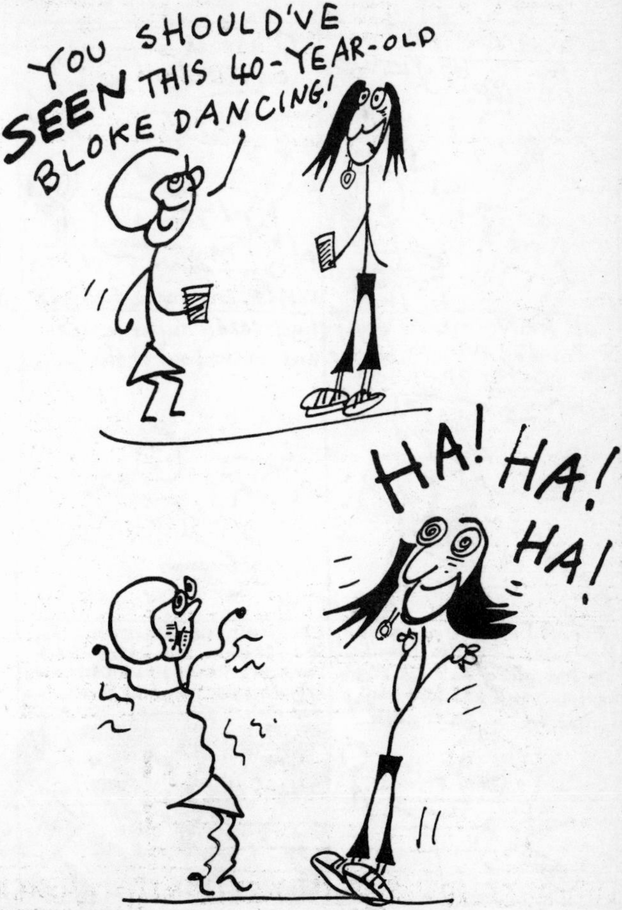
YOU SHOULD'VE SEEN THIS 40-YEAR-OLD BLOKE DANCING!
HA! HA! HA!

"I drank to drown my sorrows, but now the damned things have learned to swim..."

FRIDA KAHLO

At Every Dinnerparty...

...WHY is there
"ALWAYS ONE?

CAT PEOPLE

... talk to THEIR CATS instead of YOU!

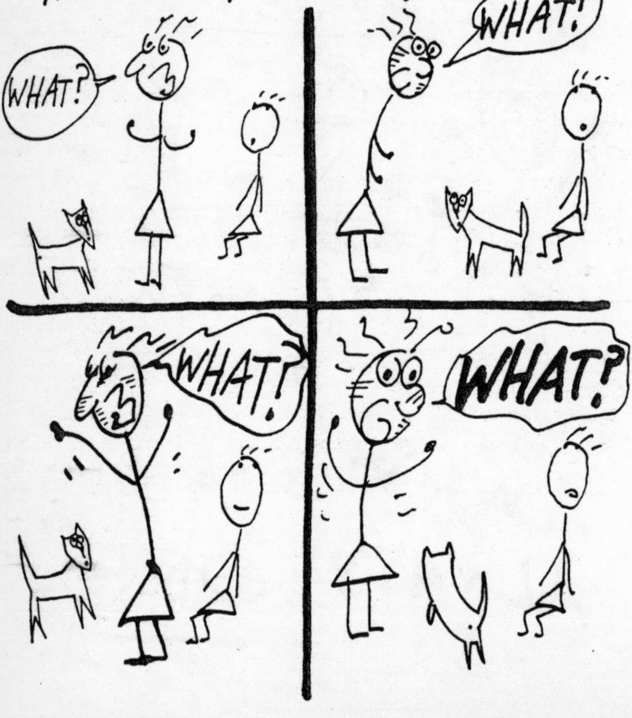

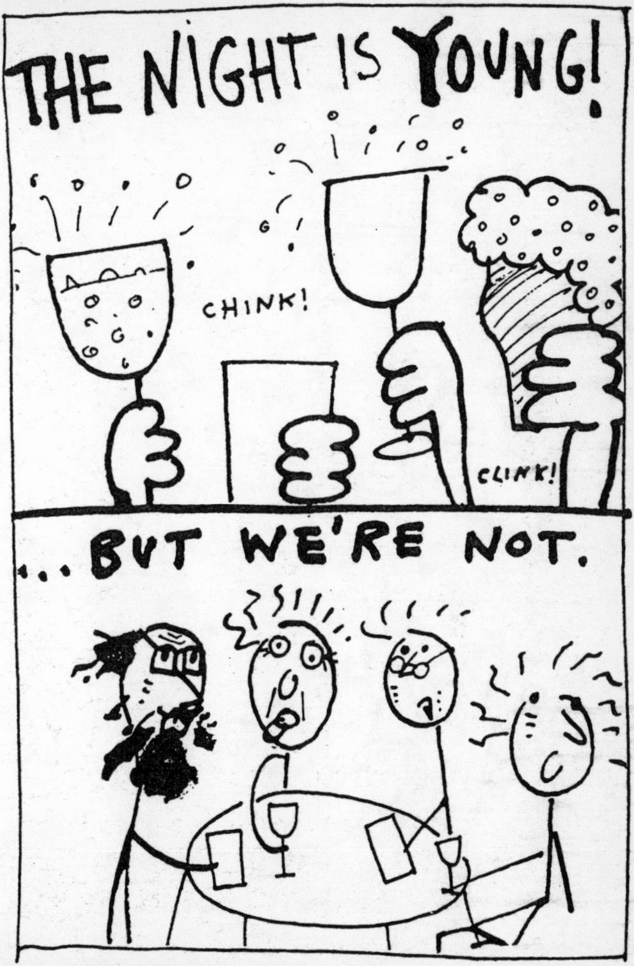
THE NIGHT IS YOUNG!
CHINK!
CLINK!
...BUT WE'RE NOT.

ALREADY
SAID IT ALL
ON THE PHONE

NITTY-GRITTY LOVE

"PARTNER"

DO YOU SAY "PARTNER" OR
DO YOU SAY "BOYFRIEND/GIRLFRIEND"?

WORK-BREAK ①

Never introduce the subject of YOUR SPOUSE into conversation with colleagues. i.e:

The Woman who loved Cats Too Much.

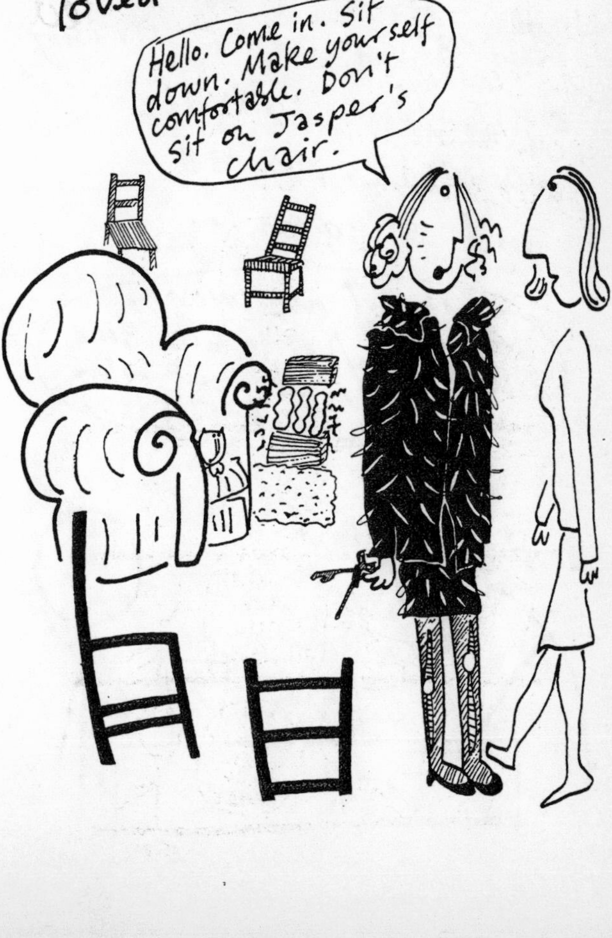

WORK-BREAK ②

Refrain from pouring out your private domestics to all and sundry...

Her Husband's Fantasy

CATWOMAN

Her Husband's Reality

WORK-BREAK ③

When you have an erotic dream about someone in the office, describe it in full detail to them the next day...

ANNIVERSARY

STILL TOGETHER AFTER ALL THESE YEARS!

ONLY BECAUSE WE'RE KNACKERED

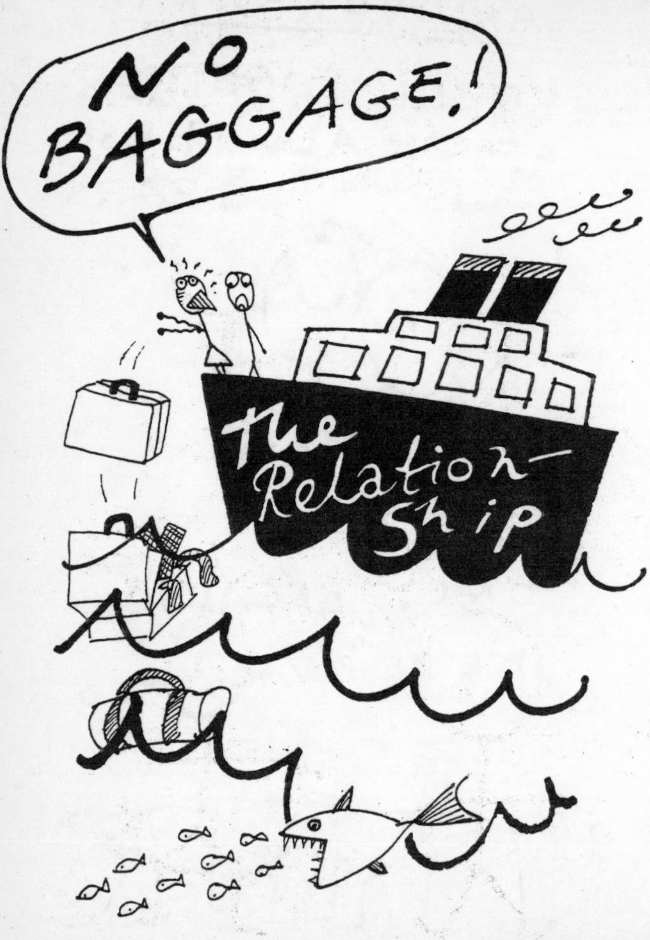
NO BAGGAGE!
the Relation-Ship

The Home-Lovers

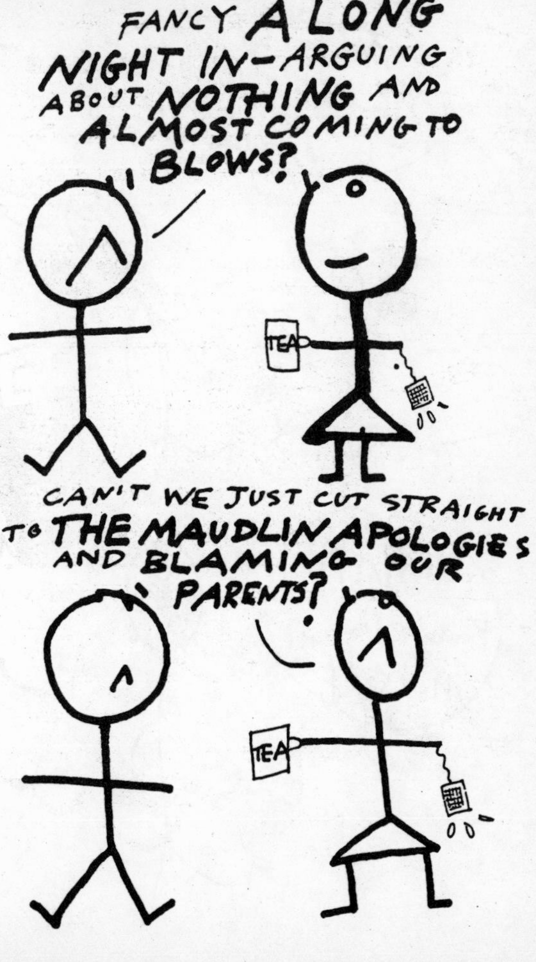

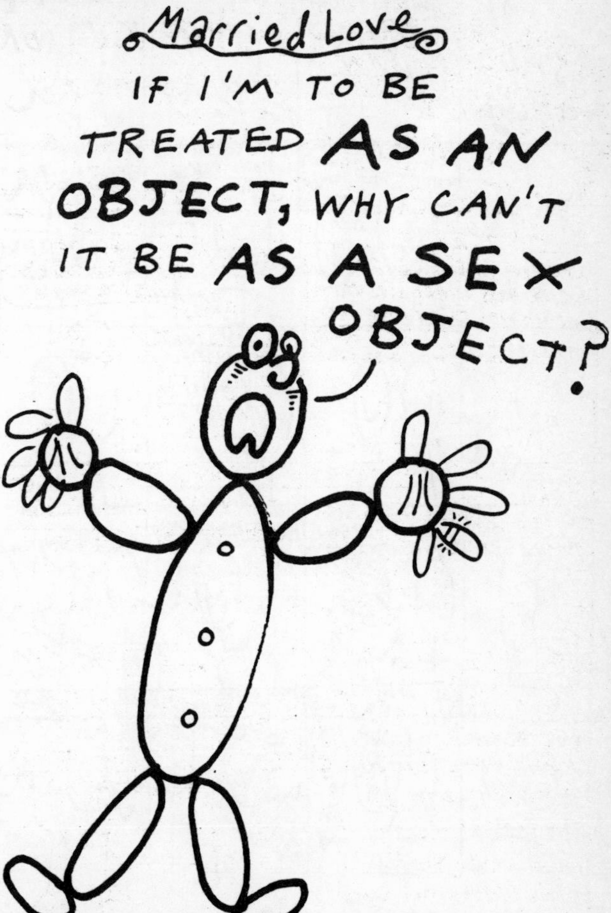
Married Love
IF I'M TO BE TREATED AS AN OBJECT, WHY CAN'T IT BE AS A SEX OBJECT?

Married Man Love
... but it's ACTUALLY TRUE ...
... his wife doesn't understand him!

When I can't get off to sleep, I imagine your arms around me.

I COME FIRST!

GET HOME. NO ONE THERE.

Oh, **THE JOY** of **THE HOUSE TO MYSELF!**

80'S REVIVAL SYNDROME
PEOPLE WHO SAY "MONEY CAN'T BUY HAPPINESS"...
...DON'T KNOW WHERE TO SHOP!
THE INDIE
POWER BUST
TARZAN
FRANKIE SAYS RELAX
FILO FAX

Hooray for my cat!

who thinks EVERYTHING I DO is fantastic.

I'M NOT GOING TO TOLERATE ANY MORE NEUROTIC, UNSORTED-OUT PEOPLE IN MY LIFE!
BUT WILL I BE BORED?

I'M LOOKING FOR A MAN WHO CAN MEET MY NEEDS

IF I "HAD IT ALL," WOULD IT BE ENOUGH?
GET "TRESSO"
BECAUSE YOU'RE WORTH IT!
WOMAN NOW!
HAVE IT ALL!

The Occasional Lovers

LET'S SEE ... WORK, WORK, WORK, TIME ON MY OWN TO RECUPERATE, WORK ...

— How about Friday?

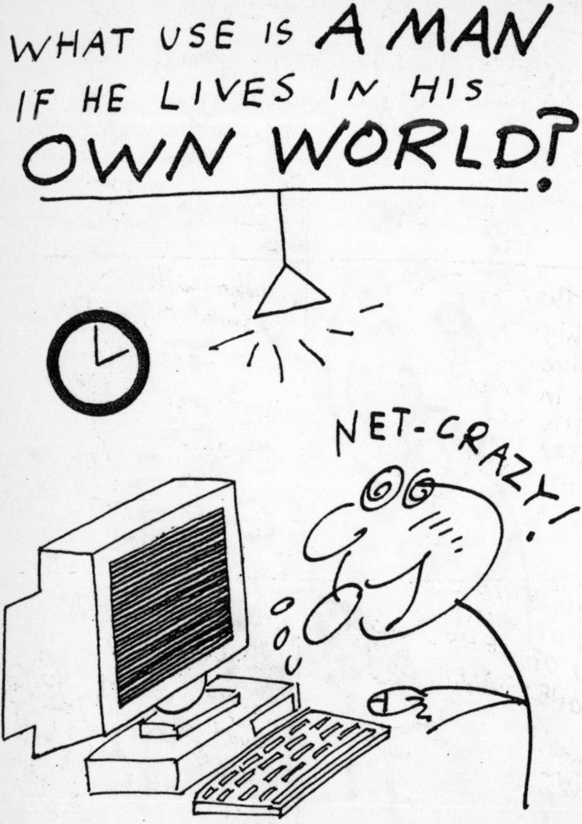
WHAT USE IS A MAN IF HE LIVES IN HIS OWN WORLD?
NET-CRAZY!

One day, IAN was in such a hurry to get to work, he forgot to FLATTEN HIS HAIR DOWN WITH TAPWATER!!!

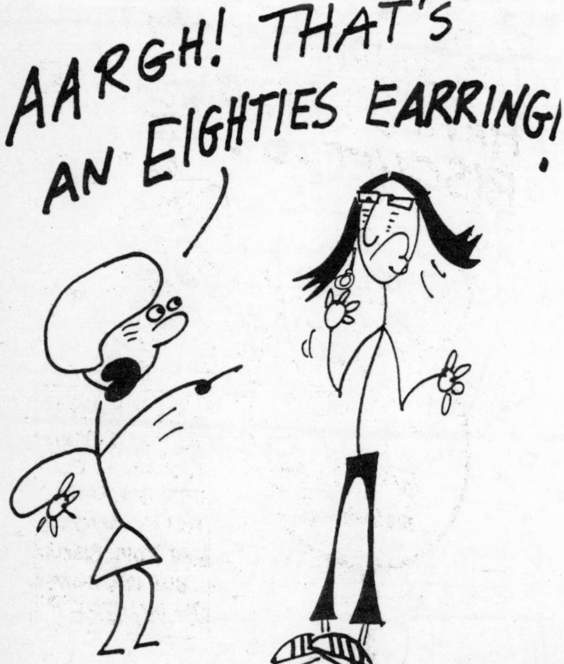
AARGH! THAT'S AN EIGHTIES EARRING!

Everyday Sensations

The Sensation of NOT HAVING EATEN 1/2 YOUR BISCUIT . . .

SCENARIO:-

YOU'RE EATING A BISCUIT. YOU GET DISTRACTED. YOU GO BACK TO EAT YOUR BISCUIT ... BUT IT'S GONE! OH WHERE?

I ♥ my CATS

I FEEL REALLY SORRY FOR PEOPLE WHO DON'T HAVE CATS... THEY HAVE TO MAKE SUCH A BIG FUSS OF THEIR CHILDREN...

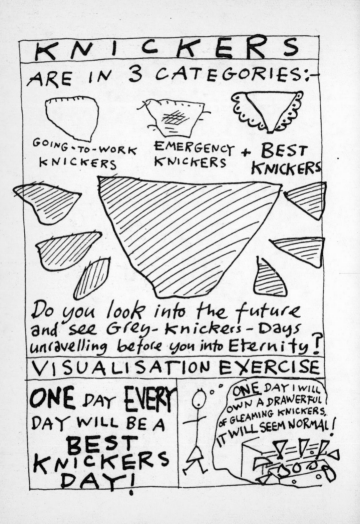